Contents

Written by **Lesley Miller**
Illustrated by **Rebecca Hallewell**
Typeset and printed by Halcon Printing, Stonehaven
Published by Kincardine & Deeside District Council
Viewmount, Stonehaven AB3 2DQ

ISBN 0952798611

The Mill in Past Years

The Mill of Benholm lies in a wooded hollow near the quiet hamlet of Benholm, which is 21km (13 miles) south of Stonehaven and 1.5km (one mile) inland from the fishing village of Johnshaven. For many centuries Benholm and hundreds of similar small mills throughout Scotland were of vital importance to the rural community as the supplier of the main food item, oatmeal. Today, Benholm is the only surviving traditional water-powered meal mill in Kincardine.

It is probable that there has been a mill at Benholm since at least the 12th century, when a charter records that William the Lion, King of the Scots, granted the lands of Benne, including its pastures, moors, woods and mills, to Hugo, who then became Hugo de Benne. A charter in 1492 gives further evidence of a mill at Benholm when John and Isabel Lundy granted the lands and barony of Benhame with the mill to their son, Robert. Later records show that the lands of Benholm, together with the mill, passed by marriage in the 16th century from the Lundy family to the Keiths, the powerful Earls Marischal. Throughout the 18th and most of the 19th century Benholm estate was owned by the Scott family before being sold to William Smith in 1879. The estate was broken up in 1905, the mill being sold with the farm of Brotherton.

It was customary in past years for the mill to be owned by the landlord, and tenant farmers were bound by their leases to take their oats to be ground at the estate mill; tenants were said to be "thirled" or "bunsucken" to that specific mill. The miller's payment, known as "the multure", was an agreed proportion of the meal ground for each tenant, or "suckener". It was often said that the miller's sow was always well fed! Tenants were also obliged to help with the maintenance of the mill and with the conveyance of new millstones when required. This latter task was particularly unpopular as the stones were heavy and cumbersome and the quarry was often some distance from the mill. Sometimes horses were employed to bring the new stone home but more often it was set on its edge and rolled homewards, controlled by men at either end of a long pole inserted through the central hole. Tenants from different estates frequently quarrelled over millstones and a report exists which tells of a fierce fight between the tenants of the Earl Marischal and those of a neighbouring estate when the Earl's men were collecting a new stone from the quarry at the Knox of Benholm in July 1617.

In 1929 the Mill of Benholm was leased to Mr Lindsay Watson. When Mr Watson died in 1951 his son, Mr Lindsay C. Watson, bought the mill and for the first time in its history the mill was owned by the miller. Many changes were to take place in the farming world during the three decades of the younger Lindsay Watson's ownership. Not least of these were the introduction of the combine harvester and the decline of oats in favour of barley. Before purpose-built grain dryers became available, the kiln at Benholm was in constant demand by local farmers during harvest time for the drying of combined barley. The market for oatmeal declined during Mr Watson's years as miller and his retail market, which had originally covered an area stretching from Barras to Laurencekirk and Montrose, dwindled. There was also a reduced demand for bruised oats for horses, now mainly replaced by the tractor. Mr Watson diversified by producing feeds mixed specifically for pigs, calves, poultry and even racing pigeons.

During Mr Watson's period of ownership the Mill of Benholm featured as the setting for several television productions. The most evocative of these was as Long Rob's Mill in the BBC production of "Sunset Song", the serialised version of the novel by local author, Lewis Grassic Gibbon. Gibbon's novel was set in his home country, the farmlands of Kincardine, and his characters, including Long Rob the Miller, were based on the folk who lived and worked here. The mill and waterwheel also provided a superb setting for televised programmes of fiddle music, one of which featured Yehudi Menuhin.

After Mr Watson's death in 1982 the Mill of Benholm slowly deteriorated as it lay silent and deserted by the stream. In 1986 it was purchased by Kincardine and Deeside District Council and the long process of restoration to working order began.

The mill buildings after restoration

The Millers of Benholm

The only requirement of the earliest millers was that they should be "good and honest men".

From Benholm Parish records it is possible to trace the names, although not the period of tenure, of the good and honest men of Benholm over a period of three hundred years.

1696	*Archibald Brown*
1706	*Robert Molison*
1720	*Alexander Steil*
1742	*William Glen*
1753	*George Smith*
1760	*Richard Dorrel*
1769	*David Milne*
1782	*David Coullie*
1784	*John Kemlo(e)*
1801	*James Mill or Milne*
1811	*James Davidson*
1836	*William Clark*
1853-1878	*James Dallas*
1878-1896	*James and David S. Dallas*
1896-1908	*David S. Dallas*
1912-1929	*William Greig*
1929-1951	*Lindsay Watson*
1951-1982	*Lindsay C. Watson*

Lindsay C. Watson and his father working on the croft

The Restoration of the Mill

The first task in the restoration process was the repair of a large hole in the lade wall caused by flooding. This and several other minor works to the weirs and stream banks were undertaken by volunteers from the Scottish Conservation Projects Trust participating in the Action Breaks Programme between 1987 and 1989.

In 1989 the restoration work began in earnest with the help of teams on government work programmes. Much of the work on underground drainage and damp-proofing the main buildings was undertaken during that period. In addition the grain store, now the miller's office, was partially rebuilt and the main mill building was re-roofed and re-floored.

Between 1991 and 1994 the old miller's house and the byre were considerably rebuilt and eventually re-roofed. During that period Whittaker Engineering of Stonehaven rebuilt and installed a new waterwheel and main cast iron gears; they also worked on the water flow from the dam and at the tailrace to ensure that water came on and off the new wheel at the correct levels.

Early in 1994 the final phase of the restoration started as a long term special project by the Scottish Conservation Projects Trust. The retaining wall of the Burn of Benholm was completely rebuilt from a point opposite the bridge over the dam down to the tailrace. Various local specialist contractors undertook roofing, electrical, drainage and fencing work. The buildings were all completed with drains installed and floors laid; the cafe and toilets were fitted out. At the same time the painstaking restoration of the mill machinery progressed.

Footpaths and bridges were constructed and the old turnpike bridge was cleared of trees and scrub and opened up for the first time in many years. The car park and reed bed were constructed by specialist local contractors. A small group of craftsmen and craftswomen from the conservation volunteers of 1994 stayed on and completed all the landscape construction and the machinery restoration during the first half of 1995.

The restoration of the Mill of Benholm took nine years to complete. All the restoration work was directed and supervised by staff from the Leisure and Recreation Section of the District Council. Those who took part in the project learned many new skills and everyone involved achieved a great sense of pride and satisfaction.

The Mill of Benholm was officially opened to the public on 6th July 1995 and a new chapter in the story of the mill began.

THE MILL TODAY

- The Mill Buildings
- The Water Source
- The Waterwheel
- The Transmission of Power
- The Croft and the Reed Bed
- Mill Brae Wood

The Mill Buildings

The present mill is a small, L-shaped two storey building, the two floors being built into the natural slope of the ground. Parts of the building date from the 18th century and the year 1711 engraved on a stone was visible until recent years. Most of the mill, however, was rebuilt in the early years of the 19th century and the lintel above the south door on the lower floor bears the date 1817 and the name, William Davidson. The present kiln, which

Carved lintel

replaced an old round kiln near the dam, has been butt-jointed onto the west end of the mill; the firebox has been built into a former doorway, the arch of which can still be seen. The cowl of the kiln is locally called the "piggy" as in past years it was often topped by a weather vane in the shape of a pig, the mill symbol.

The internal layout of the mill is of a simple design with a chain hoist and two bucket elevators to transfer the grain and its products between the two floors. Details of the kiln, millstones and mill machinery are given in a later chapter, "The Milling Process".

The cluster of buildings west of the old mill originally comprised the miller's house, the byre and the barn. The house was occupied until 1876 when a new house was built at the top of the brae for the miller, Mr James Dallas, and his family. "The auld hoose" by the stream was then used to house pigs, cattle and hens. Today it has a new role as a cafe serving visitors to the mill. The byre has been converted to toilets, the barn to a workshop and the old grain store north of the mill to the miller's office.

The mill buildings with "the auld hoose" back left

The Water Source

An adequate source of water is vital for the efficient operation of the mill. The primary power source for the Mill of Benholm is the small burn, known as the Castle Burn, that flows southwards through the Den of Benholm and tumbles down the lower weir to join its larger cousin, the Burn of Benholm. The Castle Burn supply is augmented by water brought from the Burn of Benholm through an underground aqueduct which takes water from the pool immediately above the upper weir on the Burn of Benholm. In past years an increased supply of water was sometimes obtained from the dam at Anniston Farm about one mile up the Castle Burn. The miller's boys would be sent up there on Friday evening to close the dam sluice and again on Sunday evening to open it, releasing the water to fill Benholm dam ready for milling on Monday. "Annie's Dam" now lies disused and dried up.

A dual sluice system allows water to be diverted from the burns into the man-made lade which leads to the mill dam, the reservoir of power for the mill. A full dam is sufficient to power the mill for a day's work although the amount of water actually used varies according to the nature of the work being done on any particular day. For example, more power and therefore more water is required for milling than for bruising. Less water is required in the winter when the lower temperature increases the density of the water and consequently its efficiency in driving the wheel.

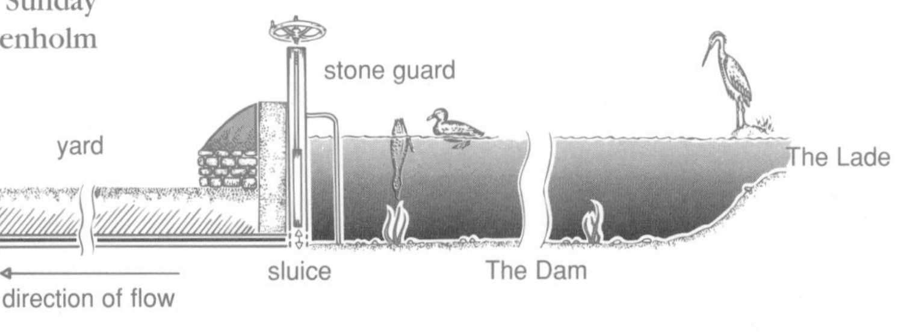

When the miller opens the sluice at the end of the dam water flows from the dam under the yard and along the metal trough, locally called the trowse (pronounced 'troose'), to the top of the waterwheel.

The Waterwheel

It is believed that the concept of harnessing water power for milling was introduced to Britain by the Romans. However, the Roman vertical waterwheel was not in widespread use in Britain until many centuries later. The type of wheel in more general use was the Greek, or Norse, horizontal wheel which was connected directly to the millstones by a vertical shaft; the wheel was turned by the flow of water against the paddles. These very basic and relatively inefficient mills were called "click mills" because of the sound they made.

Vertical waterwheels are capable of generating more power than horizontal wheels. The undershot wheel where water hits the wheel at a height no greater than 8 o' clock is the least efficient vertical type. It is turned in an anti-clockwise direction purely by the force of the water flow. Early models had flat paddles but these were later improved to resemble open-ended buckets.

The breastshot, or breast, wheel is one where water strikes the wheel at axle level. It is driven by the weight of water in the buckets, not by the force of the flow. A similar type of wheel is the backshot or pitch-back; here the water is brought along a trough to hit the wheel just before the top centre point. Both these types of wheel turn anti-clockwise.

The most efficient wheel is the overshot, as at Benholm. Water is carried along a trough to hit the wheel just beyond its top centre point. As in the breastshot and backshot types, the wheel is turned by the weight of water in the buckets but in this case in a clockwise direction. It has been calculated that the overshot wheel is two and a half times more efficient and needs only a quarter of the water required by the undershot wheel.

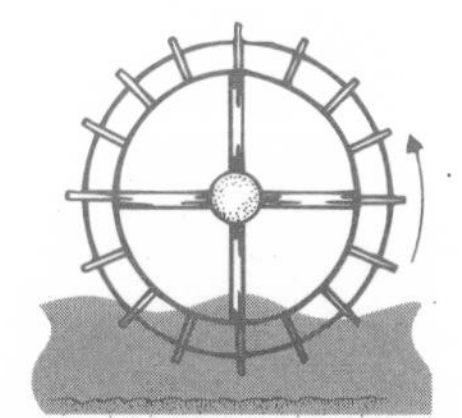

Early Undershot Wheel

The Breastshot Wheel

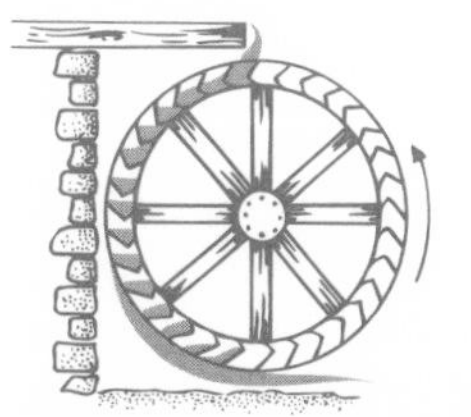

The Backshot or Pitch-back Wheel

The Overshot Wheel

The present waterwheel at Benholm was built and installed during the restoration of the mill. Like its predecessor, it is overshot, water falling from the trowse to hit the wheel just beyond its top centre point. Traces have, however, been found of a much earlier undershot wheel which was sited by the Burn of Benholm near the end of the present tailrace.

The wheel has 32 wooden buckets around the perimeter. The power output depends on the weight of water transported and the height through which it falls while in the buckets. For maximum efficiency buckets should be as wide as possible and designed so that they do not spill water until very near the tailrace. Larch and willow were the woods traditionally used for buckets.

The wheel is 12 feet (366 cm) in diameter and 40 inches (102 cm) wide with eight wooden spokes. The axle bushes are made of phosphor bronze which has a very high tensile strength. The output of the wheel is equivalent to approximately eight horse power.

A steel axle connects the waterwheel to the pit wheel inside the mill. The term, axle tree, is still sometimes used because mill axles were made of oak, ash or elm in the past. It is customary for the mill wall next to the waterwheel to be built more strongly than the other walls as the masonry has to withstand the vibration of the turning waterwheel.

Water falls from the buckets into the tailrace which leads to the Burn of Benholm. The tailrace slopes downwards from below the centre of the wheel so that water runs off quickly and does not cause resistance to the wheel. A sluice on the trowse can be closed to divert water away from the wheel and into the bypass channel which leads into the tailrace.

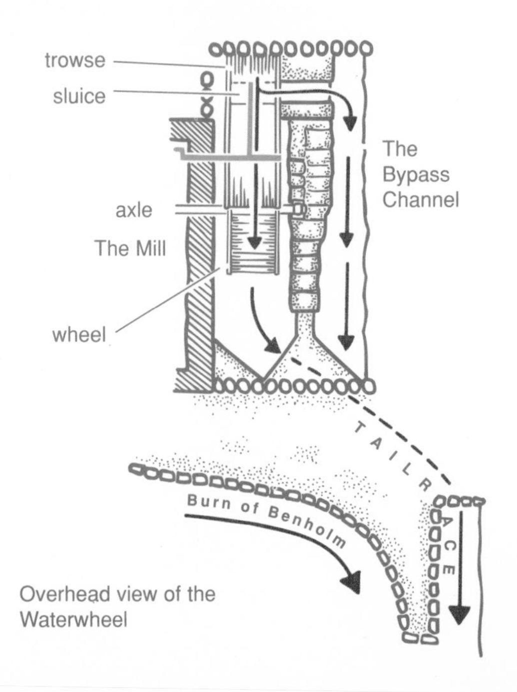

Overhead view of the Waterwheel

The Transmission of Power

Although the arrangement and complexity of the gears vary from mill to mill, the basic principle of transmitting power from the waterwheel via the axle to the pit wheel and hence through a series of cogged wheels, or gears, to the mill machinery is fundamental to all mills. The gears at Benholm are illustrated below.

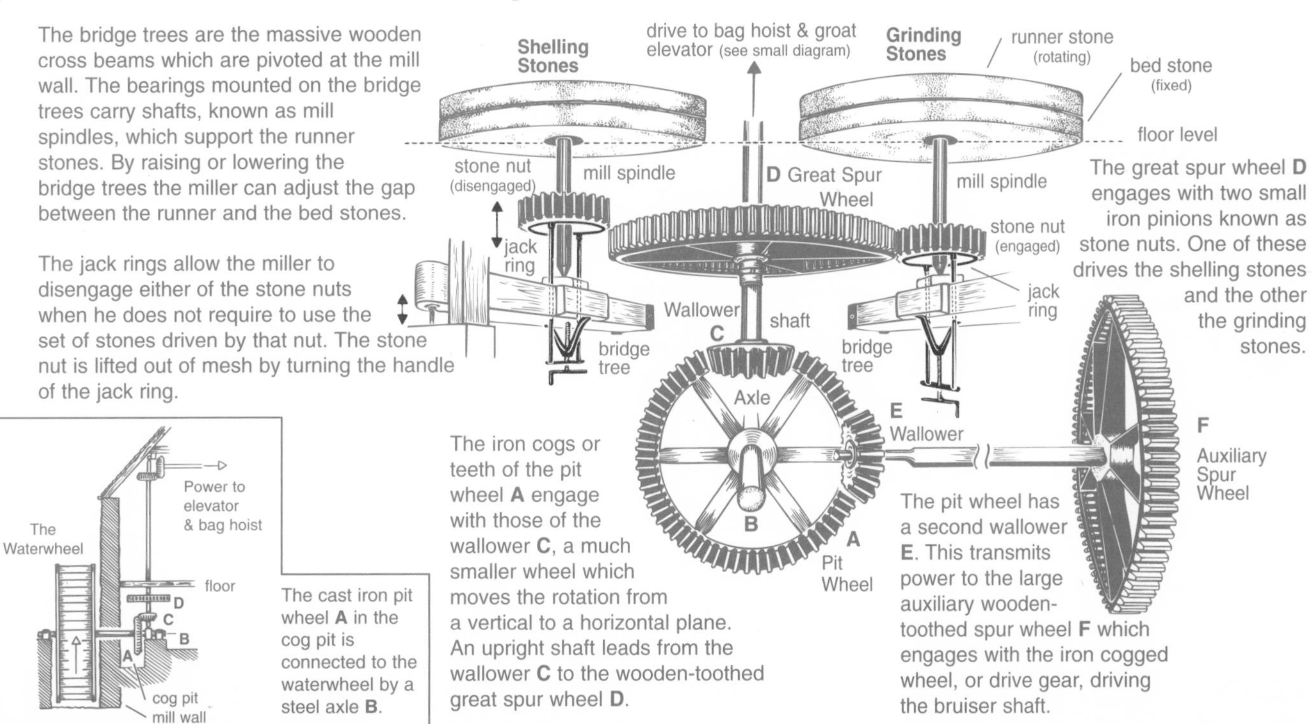

The bridge trees are the massive wooden cross beams which are pivoted at the mill wall. The bearings mounted on the bridge trees carry shafts, known as mill spindles, which support the runner stones. By raising or lowering the bridge trees the miller can adjust the gap between the runner and the bed stones.

The jack rings allow the miller to disengage either of the stone nuts when he does not require to use the set of stones driven by that nut. The stone nut is lifted out of mesh by turning the handle of the jack ring.

The great spur wheel **D** engages with two small iron pinions known as stone nuts. One of these drives the shelling stones and the other the grinding stones.

The cast iron pit wheel **A** in the cog pit is connected to the waterwheel by a steel axle **B**.

The iron cogs or teeth of the pit wheel **A** engage with those of the wallower **C**, a much smaller wheel which moves the rotation from a vertical to a horizontal plane. An upright shaft leads from the wallower **C** to the wooden-toothed great spur wheel **D**.

The pit wheel has a second wallower **E**. This transmits power to the large auxiliary wooden-toothed spur wheel **F** which engages with the iron cogged wheel, or drive gear, driving the bruiser shaft.

The Croft & Reed Bed

The Croft

The miller was traditionally granted a small area of land alongside the mill which gave him an additional source of income. At Benholm the miller's croft, extends to 7.5 acres (3 hectares), sufficient for the miller to cultivate oats in addition to keeping cows, pigs and hens.

Farm animals, including some rare breeds, can be seen here. Traditional farm crops, such as bere, a primitive form of barley, and old varieties of vegetables and fruit bushes are organically grown. A small tree and wild flower nursery has been established.

The Reed Bed

Wastewaters from the cafe and toilets undergo primary treatment in a septic tank and secondary treatment in the reed bed which has been constructed to ensure that no pollutants are discharged into the Burn of Benholm.

The bed has been planted with the common reed, *Phragmites australis*, a perennial plant which occurs naturally throughout Britain.

The vigorous root and rhizome system of the reeds acts as a filter for solids suspended in the effluent which is pumped up from the septic tank. The supply of oxygen in the root system and in the fine pea gravel of the bed creates a suitable habitat for the aerobic bacteria which break down the organic waste products. These micro-organisms absorb organic particles and convert them to carbon dioxide, water and ammonia compounds.

The nutrients are absorbed by the reeds and the mineralised solids are retained in the bed. A layer of sludge and decomposing vegetation gradually builds up in the reed bed and provides a food source for the micro-organism population over periods when no sewage is being discharged.

The reeds, which grow up to two metres tall when mature, lose their leaves in winter but the dead stalks stand erect for several seasons.

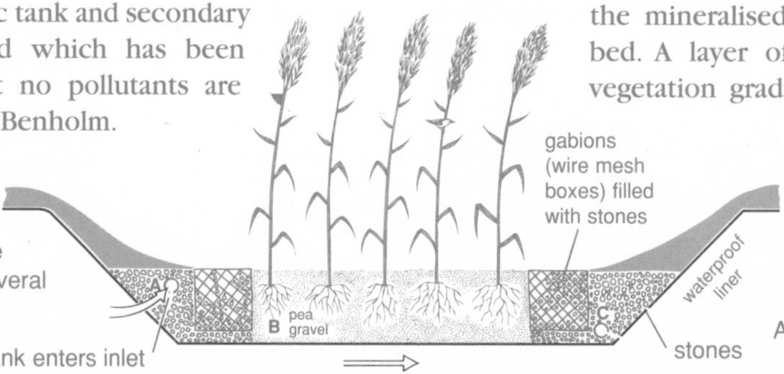

gabions (wire mesh boxes) filled with stones

Treated effluent from the septic tank enters inlet pipe **A**.

Effluent percolates slowly from slots in pipe **A** and flows through the reed bed **B**.

After several days the final effluent from the slotted outlet pipe **C** is discharged into the Burn of Benholm.

Mill Brae Wood

The woodland walk

A footbridge over the Burn of Benholm leads to the ancient woodland which has over-shadowed the mill for centuries. A path wends eastwards through the wood to the old Benholm Bridge, built to carry the early 19th century turnpike road across the deep gorge of the burn. In bygone days people making their way on foot to the hamlet of Benholm came through the wood, past the mill and along the path by the lade and the Castle Burn.

The wood is semi-natural and is unusual for the region in that it is composed mainly of wych elm and ash. Scattered through the wood are sycamore, gean, larch, hazel and Norway maple. Beech trees around the periphery of the wood were probably planted about one hundred years ago. Wild gooseberry bushes, lady fern, male fern and wood-rush grow abundantly below the canopy.

A profusion of plants cover the floor of the woodland. These include the dog's mercury and the common nettle, both of which have small inconspicuous flowers. More colourful are the red campion, the primrose, the creeping buttercup and the early-purple orchid. Alongside the banks of the Burn of Benholm lesser celandine, lords and ladies, and marsh marigold bloom. Butterburr, which flowers in early spring and produces large leaves after the flowers have died back, also grows by the stream.

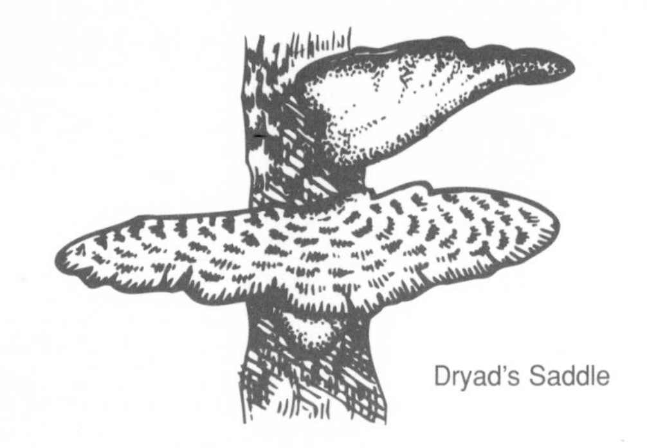

Dryad's Saddle

Many species of fungi flourish in the wood. One of the most prominent is the dryad's saddle, which produces a thick fan-shaped growth on the trunks of deciduous trees and causes white rot. Also common in the wood is the honey fungus, or boot-lace fungus, which grows in clusters on and around tree trunks and stumps. The honey fungus plays a significant role in the ecology of the woodland. It forms an association with the early-purple orchid but does not appear to harm it. It does, however, kill both very old trees and seedlings which it parasitises. It spreads by means of long black cords, or rhizomorphs, which resemble boot laces and which invade the trees causing them to rot and die. These dead trees and branches are an important feature of the wood as they provide an ideal habitat for innumerable invertebrates such as spiders, beetles and other insects.

The insects which live in both the dead and the living trees are an ample source of food for song birds nesting in the wood. Rooks also nest here, the droppings from the rookery enriching the soil with nitrogen. Pigeons, wrens, robins, tree creepers and blackbirds are commonly seen. Numerous rabbits live in the wood, foxes pass through on hunting expeditions and roe deer occasionally come down to the stream to drink. Because pressure of grazing prevents natural regeneration of the trees, seeds are being collected, germinated and grown in the tree nursery to be eventually replanted in the wood with protection from rabbits.

Wren - reddish/brown with white throat, 9.5cms long.

Wood Pigeon - blue/grey with purple throat, 40cms long.

The mill buildings at an early stage during the restoration (left), and after completion of all the work (below)

The Milling Process at the Mill of Benholm

The basic process of converting oats to oatmeal by drying, shelling, separating, grinding and sieving is similar at every meal mill. However, no two mills are identical and details of the milling process vary according to the shape, size and lay-out of each mill and its machinery. The diagram illustrates the complete milling process at the Mill of Benholm from the delivery of dressed oats ready for drying to the production of the required grade of oatmeal.

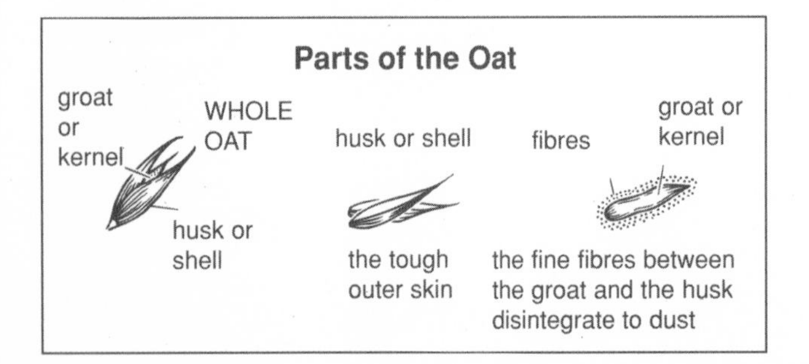

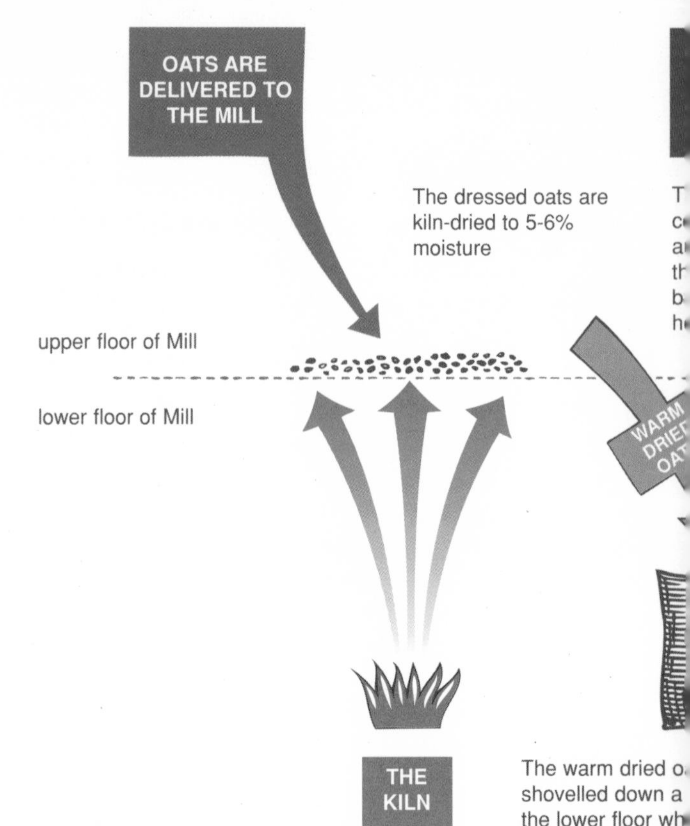

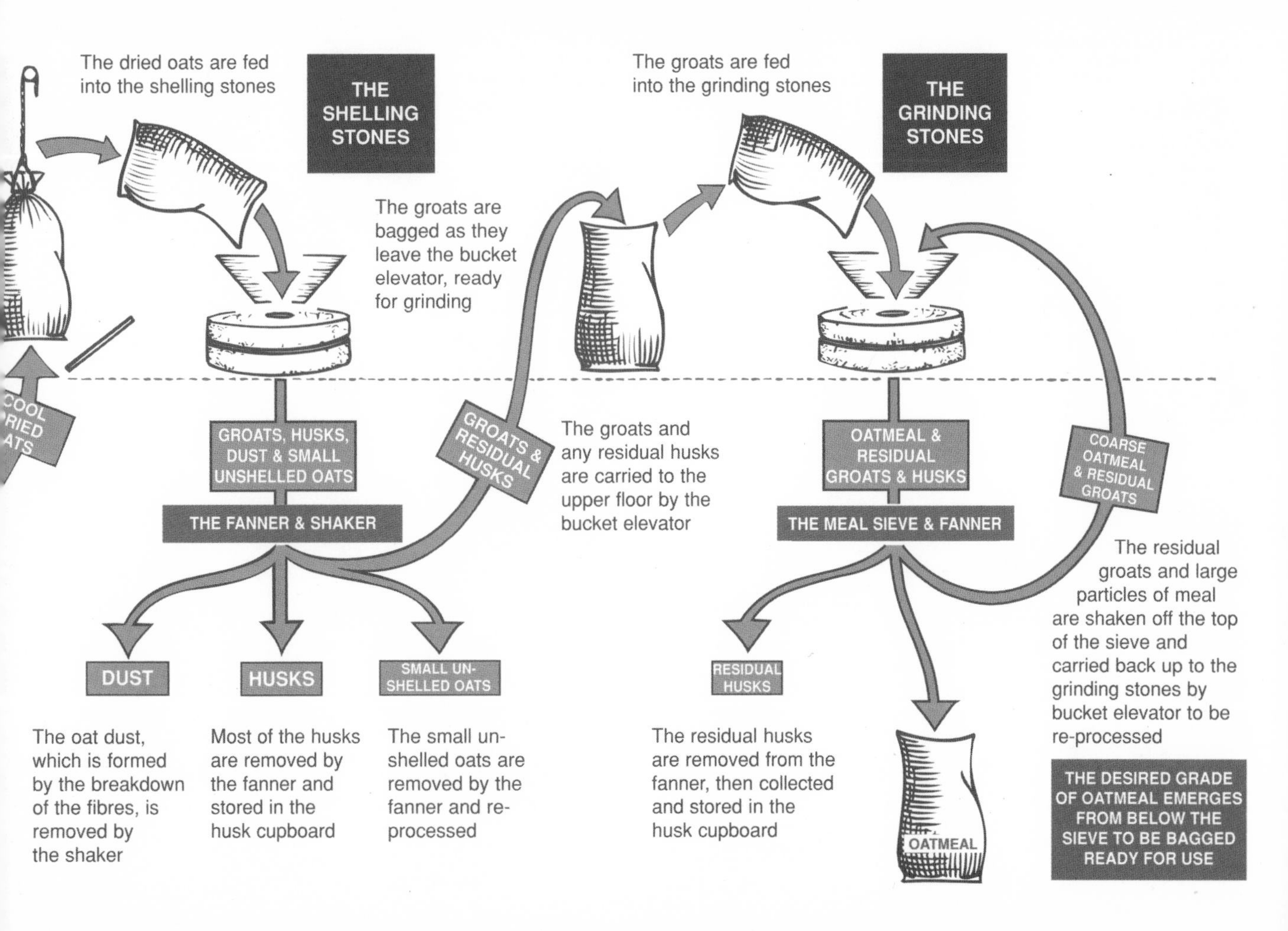

The dried oats are fed into the shelling stones
THE SHELLING STONES
The groats are bagged as they leave the bucket elevator, ready for grinding
COOL DRIED OATS
GROATS, HUSKS, DUST & SMALL UNSHELLED OATS
THE FANNER & SHAKER
GROATS & RESIDUAL HUSKS
DUST
HUSKS
SMALL UN-SHELLED OATS
The oat dust, which is formed by the breakdown of the fibres, is removed by the shaker
Most of the husks are removed by the fanner and stored in the husk cupboard
The small un-shelled oats are removed by the fanner and re-processed
The groats are fed into the grinding stones
THE GRINDING STONES
The groats and any residual husks are carried to the upper floor by the bucket elevator
OATMEAL & RESIDUAL GROATS & HUSKS
THE MEAL SIEVE & FANNER
COARSE OATMEAL & RESIDUAL GROATS
The residual groats and large particles of meal are shaken off the top of the sieve and carried back up to the grinding stones by bucket elevator to be re-processed
RESIDUAL HUSKS
The residual husks are removed from the fanner, then collected and stored in the husk cupboard
OATMEAL
THE DESIRED GRADE OF OATMEAL EMERGES FROM BELOW THE SIEVE TO BE BAGGED READY FOR USE

The upper floor showing the bucket elevators, the chain hoist and the tuns

The miller inspecting some oatmeal

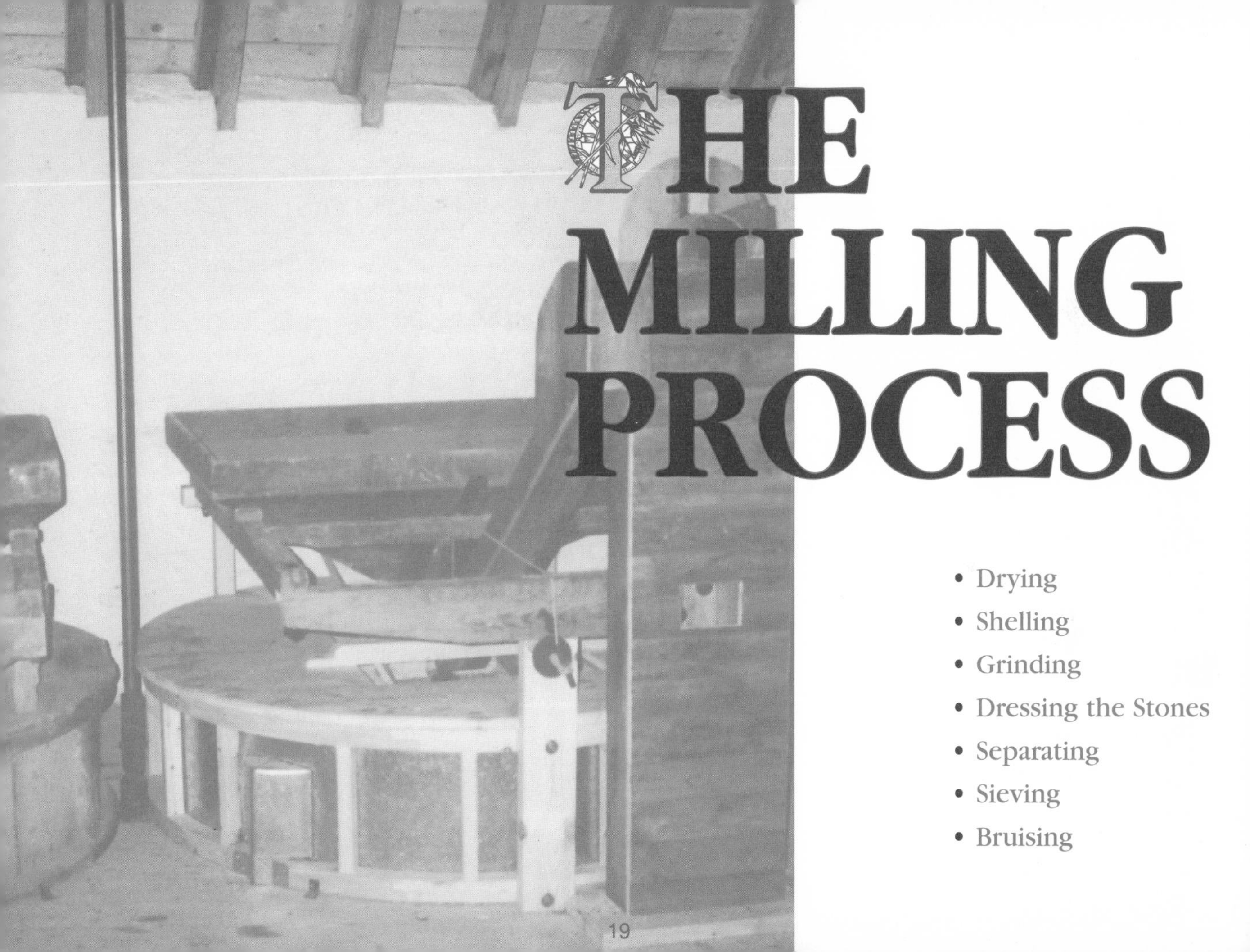

THE MILLING PROCESS

- Drying
- Shelling
- Grinding
- Dressing the Stones
- Separating
- Sieving
- Bruising

Drying

The kiln-drying of oats is one of the most important processes in the production of oatmeal. It is not a precise science but a skilled operation which a miller learns by experience. Careful drying in the kiln toasts the oats and gives the meal the desired nutty flavour and aroma.

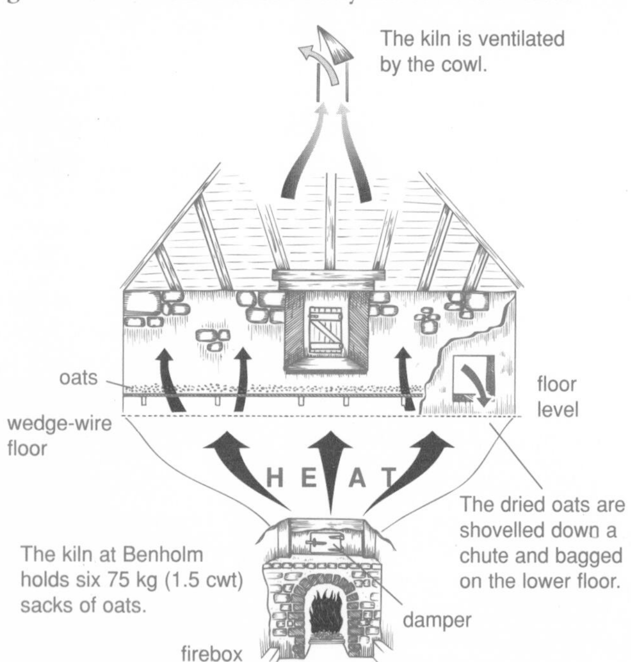

The moisture content of grain arriving at the mill for drying is around 18%. This is reduced to approximately 5%. Oats coming direct from a combine harvester, without going through a grain drier, have a much higher moisture content than oats in past years which were sheaved, stooked, rucked and thrashed.

Anthracite is the fuel now most commonly used but coke, peat or husks were used in the past. Husks may still be utilised to kindle the fire and may also be added during the drying process to give extra flavour and sweetness to the oatmeal. When the temperature at the kiln floor is approximately 115°F the oats are spread over the wedge-wire to a depth of 10 cm (4 inches). The temperature is then gradually raised to 180°.

The drying process takes approximately four hours. During this time the grain is turned twice with a long-handled wooden shovel, an onerous task in the hot and, during the early part of the process, steamy atmosphere of the kiln. The heat of the kiln floor is so intense that the miller or "dryster" in charge of the kilning process wears wooden-soled boots. Blackened beams around the kiln door are the result of a fire in 1971. The oats are removed from the kiln whilst still hot and the kiln is then allowed to cool to around 115°F before the next batch of oats is spread.

Shelling

The Mill of Benholm has two sets of millstones, each enclosed within a wooden casing called the tun. The dried oats first pass through the shelling stones which remove the shells, or husks, from the kernels. The kernels, or groats, are then ground into oatmeal in the grinding stones. Each set of stones consists of a stationary bed stone and a runner stone above it which is rotated by the mill spindle. An unusual feature of this mill is that the stones rotate in an anti-clockwise direction.

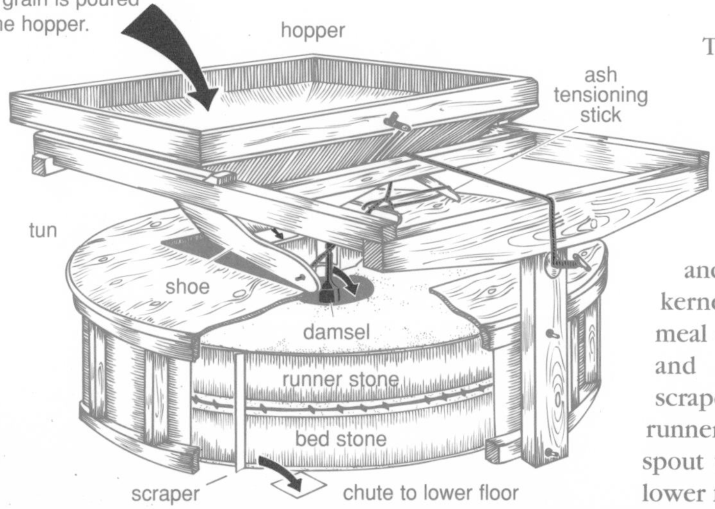

Dried grain is poured into the hopper.

hopper

ash tensioning stick

tun

shoe

damsel

runner stone

bed stone

scraper

chute to lower floor

The grain drops through the hopper above the shelling stones onto a tilted wooden tray known as the shoe. To ensure a steady flow of grain into the eye of the stone, the shoe is shaken by the damsel, a metal shaft widened at the centre into two beaters. It is attached to the top of the spindle and as it rotates with the runner stone the beaters repeatedly knock the shoe to one side. The shoe is jerked back to its original position by a springy ash stick. The damsel is often called "the clappers" because of the clacking sound it makes.

The shelling stones at Benholm are monolithic gritstones, 47 inches (120 cm) in diameter, which have been refaced with carborundum. The gap between the bed stone and the runner stone is set so that the oats, which are elongated in shape, bounce between the two stones. The shells, or husks, crack and drop off, and the fibrous material between the shell and the kernel disintegrates to dust. The kernels, husks and meal dust are conveyed to the periphery of the stones and drop into the wooden casing. Two metal scrapers attached to the outer rim of the rotating runner stone sweep all the material down the outlet spout to be separated in the fanner and shaker on the lower floor.

Grinding

French burr stone is chalcedonic hornstone, an unusual type of quartz which occurs only in central France. This exceptionally hard stone was in great demand for milling from the late 18th century onwards but is no longer quarried. Burr stone was extracted in small pieces which were trimmed and fitted together with plaster of Paris within an iron band to form a millstone with especially sharp grinding edges.

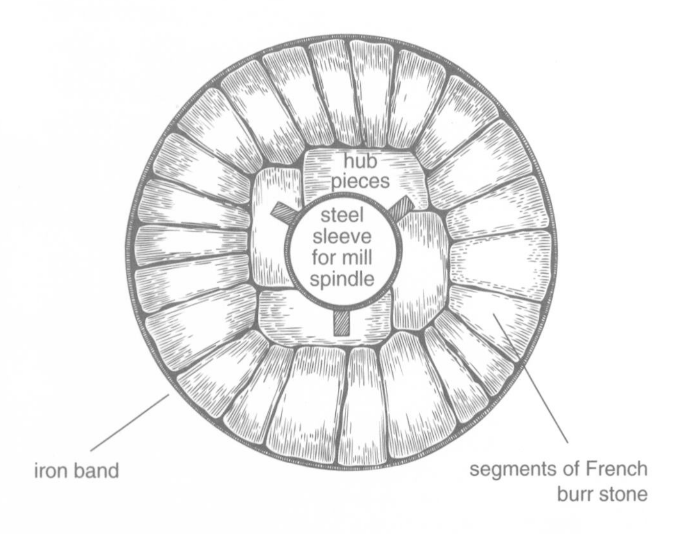

Grinding Stone

After separation from the husks and dust in the fanner and shaker, the kernels, or groats, are transported back to the upper floor by the groats bucket elevator, which is driven by the mitre gears in the roof space. The groats are then bagged and carried to the hopper which feeds into the grinding stones. These are 55 inches (140 cm) in diameter and are composed of segments of French burr stone. The gap between the two grinding stones is smaller than that between the shelling stones and is adjusted according to the grade of oatmeal being produced.

The surface of each grinding stone is segmented into ten areas known as harps. Each harp is divided by four furrows, or roads, the flat areas between them being called lands. The sharp edges of the lands meet in a scissors type action which grinds the kernels into meal. The meal, along with any incompletely ground groats and residual husks, is channelled along the furrows to the periphery of the stones where it drops into the tun and is swept down the spout by the scrapers. This mixture drops into the meal sieve and fanner on the lower floor to be separated. Any unground groats and very large pieces of meal are immediately transported upwards by the smaller bucket elevator and dropped into the grinding stones again.

Dressing the Stones

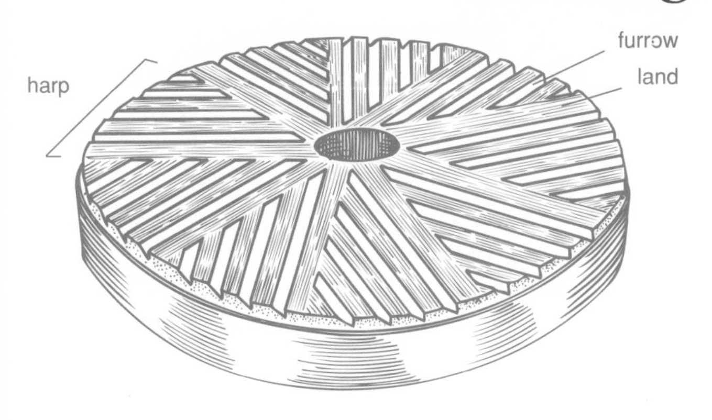

Milling stones require regular care and attention in order to maintain efficient grinding. The miller must always ensure that the stones are properly balanced with an even gap between them to avoid irregular grinding and wear of the stones. In addition, the stones have to be dressed periodically. Although a local millwright was sometimes employed for this skilled task, many millers, including Mr Watson at Benholm and his father before him, dressed their own stones.

Before dressing commences the runner stone is lifted off the spindle and upturned so that the grinding faces of both stones are exposed. The surfaces are first checked for uneven wear by moving a straight-edged staff painted with coloured paste across the stones so that any upstanding parts become smeared with the paste; these are then smoothed down to give a level surface. The furrows, which distribute the meal away from the centre of the stone, are deepened and the grinding edges of the lands, which cut the groats, are sharpened. The very fine grooves on the surface of the lands, which are sometimes known as the harp strings, are then painstakingly recut with a small pick, a process known as "cracking".

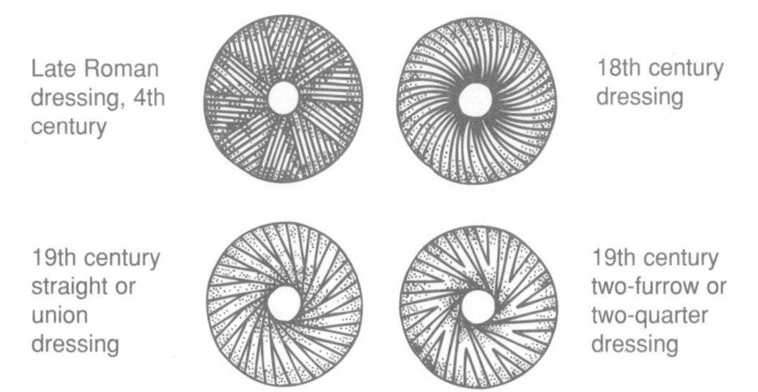

Several standard patterns of stone dressing have been recorded throughout the history of milling. The pattern most commonly found today closely resembles that used in Roman times.

Separating

From the shelling stones on the upper floor a mixture of shelled oats (now called groats), unshelled oats, husks and dust drop from a spout onto the shaker. The dust is sieved out by the shaker whilst the other materials are carried along and drop into the fanner to be separated by the flow of air generated by the paddles.

The vibratory motion of the shaker causes the meal dust to fall through the sieve; it is then bagged at chute **A**. The groats, the unshelled small oats and the husks are carried along the surface of the sieve to the far end **B** where they fall into the fanner. The groats, which are the heaviest material, drop into the first hopper which feeds into the bottom of the bucket elevator. The husks and unshelled small oats are lighter than the groats and are blown up the ramp by the air flow generated by the paddles. The unshelled oats drop into the second hopper and are removed at trapdoor **C**. The husks, which are the lightest material, are blown right across both hoppers and into the husk cupboard.

The husks, which comprise 25% of the weight of the oats, can be used as animal feed. A handful may be added to the kiln fire to sweeten the flavour of the oatmeal. In the past husks were also used to make sowens. The husks were steeped in water for one to two weeks so that the fine flour from the inner husk, known as sids, separated off as sediment. This was strained off and boiled to give a nutritious dish, traditionally supped with a horn spoon.

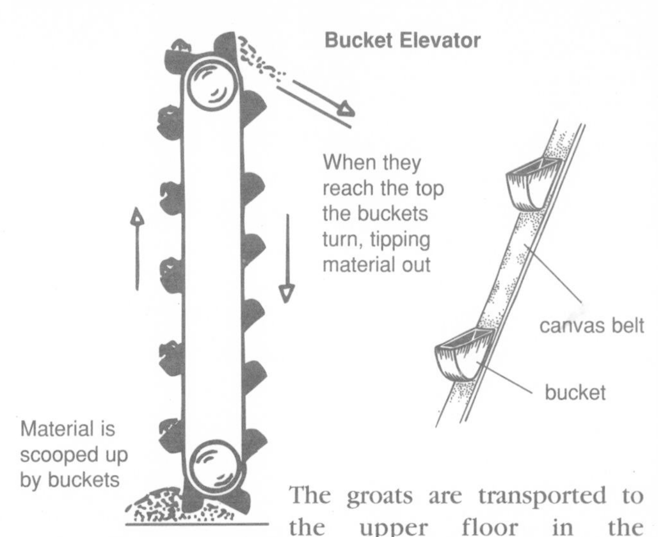

The groats are transported to the upper floor in the continuous-flow bucket elevator, which is enclosed in a wooden casing. The groats are carried in a series of small metal cups (buckets) spaced along a strengthened canvas belt. On the upper floor the groats are bagged and carried to the grinding stones to be ground into oatmeal.

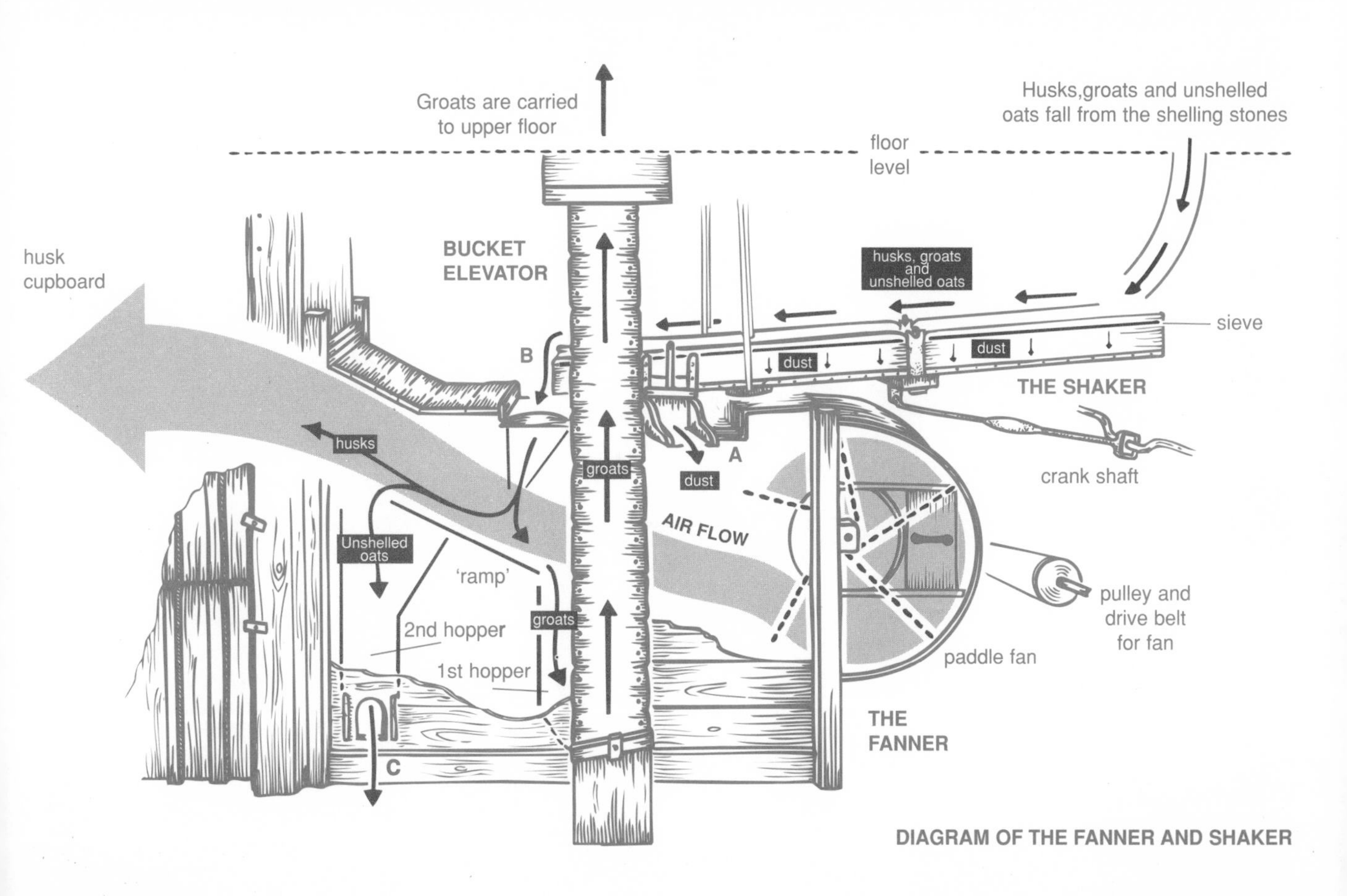

DIAGRAM OF THE FANNER AND SHAKER

Sieving

The function of the meal sieve and small fanner is to remove any remaining unground groats and husks from the end product, the oatmeal, and to sieve the meal to the required grade.

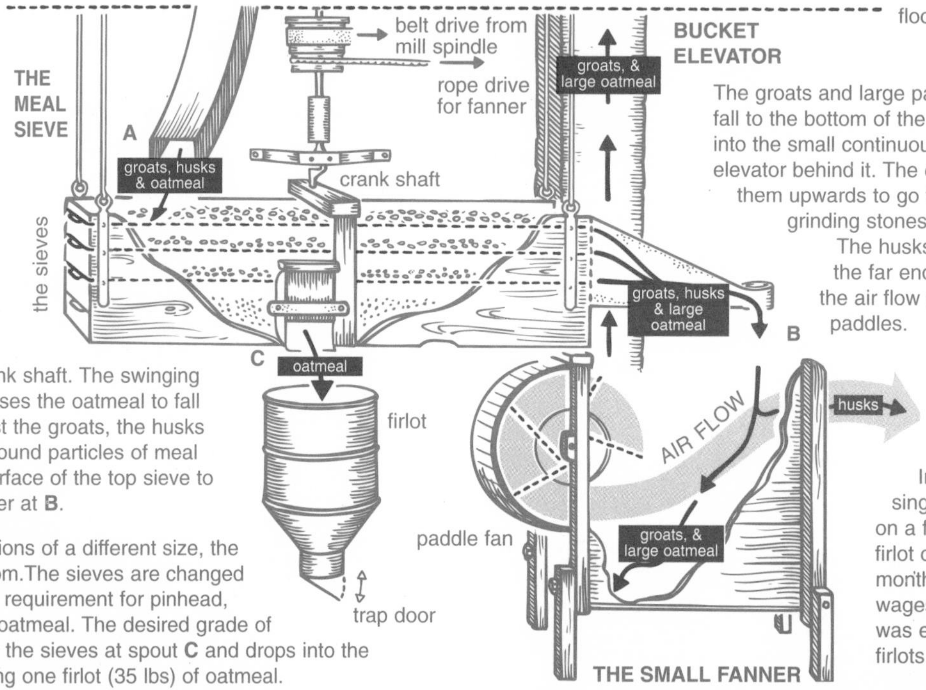

The oatmeal, unground groats and small husks emerge from the grinding stones at spout **A** and fall onto the meal sieve. The sieve consists of a series of wiremesh sieves fitted like drawers within a box which is suspended from above and shaken in a circular motion by a crank shaft. The swinging and shaking motion causes the oatmeal to fall through the sieves whilst the groats, the husks and any insufficiently ground particles of meal are carried along the surface of the top sieve to drop into the small fanner at **B**.

Each sieve has perforations of a different size, the finest being on the bottom.The sieves are changed according to the miller's requirement for pinhead, coarse, medium or fine oatmeal. The desired grade of oatmeal emerges below the sieves at spout **C** and drops into the firlot, a receptacle holding one firlot (35 lbs) of oatmeal.

The groats and large particles of meal fall to the bottom of the fanner and feed into the small continuous-flow bucket elevator behind it. The elevator carries them upwards to go through the grinding stones a second time. The husks are blown out of the far end of the fanner by the air flow generated by the paddles.

In past times a single man working on a farm received one firlot of oatmeal per month as part of his wages; a married man was entitled to two firlots.

Bruising

The bruiser produces bruised and gristed oats from grain which has not been kiln-dried or shelled. The oats are fed into hopper **A** on the upper floor and drop into hopper **B**. Both hoppers are divided in two, one half feeding the bruiser and the other the grister. Bruised (or crushed) oats are made by rolling which flattens the oats to yield a rough and abrasive product sold as feed for horses and cattle. Gristed (or kibbled) oats are made by grinding between two discs **C** to give a fine gritty product often used as poultry feed. Barley, peas and beans may also be processed.

Power from the waterwheel is transmitted to the bruiser from a drive shaft by means of a pulley and belt system. Mr Lindsay Watson conserved water power by using a stationary engine or tractor based in an outside shed to run the bruiser.

The production of animal feed using the bruiser and grister was an important part of Mr Watson's trade. He sold bruised and gristed oats and barley direct from the bruiser and also made his own feeding compounds by mixing the bruised and gristed products with bought-in materials such as molasses, flaked maize, wheat, peas and beans. The feeding stuffs were specifically mixed and sold for different animals, including calves, pigs, poultry and racing pigeons.

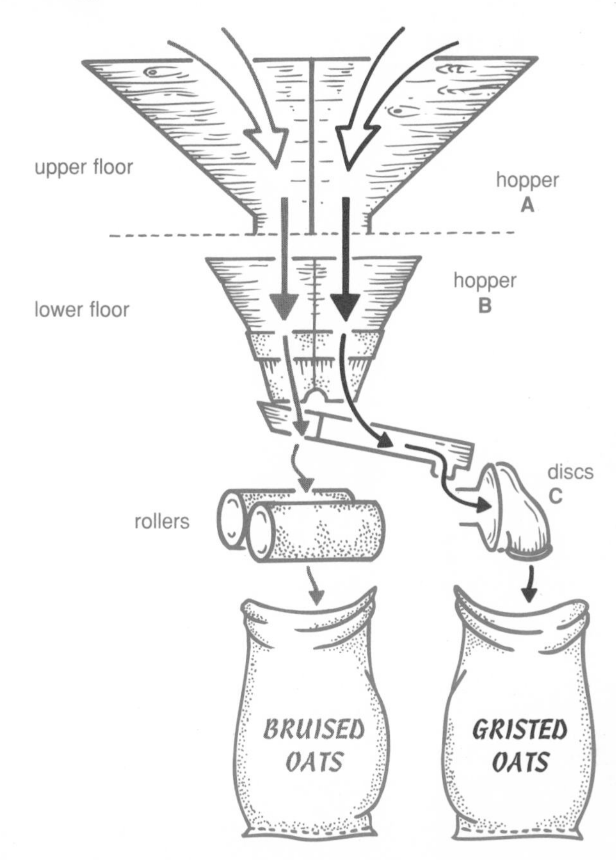

THE STORY OF OATS & OATMEAL

- Oats and Oatmeal
- Recipes using Oatmeal

Oats and Oatmeal

The climate and soil in Scotland are ideal for the cultivation of oats and Scottish grown oats are renowned for their quality and flavour. Growth is comparatively slow in the cool moist climate, allowing the oat kernels to become plump before ripening.

Today's cultivated varieties are derived from the wild oat which originated in southeast Europe and western Asia. Although oats were cultivated in central Europe from around 1000 BC they were not grown in Scotland until about 100 BC. By the 13th century oats were firmly established as a Scottish crop although bere, a primitive form of barley, remained the most widely grown cereal until the late 17th century. The improvement of farming practices and the introduction of new varieties of oats during the 18th and 19th centuries led to a rapid increase in the acreage of cultivated oats and oatmeal became established as a staple item of the Scottish diet.

The drovers subsisted on oatmeal

For over 150 years the oat was the most extensively cultivated cereal in Scotland and provided the basic fare for both man and beast. It supplied a nutritious and palatable straw for animals in addition to the grain which, when crushed or ground, provided high quality feed for horses, cattle, sheep, pigs and poultry. In the mid 20th century the decline of the working horse with the introduction of the tractor, and the rising popularity of barley as a crop led to a vast reduction in the acreage of oats sown. In recent years there has been an upturn in the amount of oats grown due to fresh publicity given to the important health-giving properties of oatmeal.

The value of oats as a convenient and nourishing food for man as well as livestock has, however, long been appreciated by the Scots. As early as the 14th century it is recorded that Scottish soldiers carried oatmeal which they mixed with a little water and heated on a metal plate to make a form of oatcake. The drovers, many of whom walked hundreds of miles when taking cattle to the Lowland markets, subsisted almost entirely on oatmeal during their trek. Apprentices and students brought their own supplies to their lodgings and it was only in the mid 20th century that the Scottish Universities abolished Meal Monday, the traditional January holiday when students returned home to replenish their supplies.

The rural diet was based on oatmeal.

For many years oatmeal was a form of currency and it was customary for tenant farmers to pay their rent in meal. The miller too was paid with a proportion of meal from each load milled. Meal comprised a substantial portion of the wages of the farmworker and even the minister, the schoolmaster and the postman received an allocation of meal to supplement their salaries. Oatmeal was acceptable as part of a dowry too. It has been said: "There was never a time in Scotland's history when a little meal in your poke was not better than coin in your pouch".

Oats may be eaten as oatmeal, rolled oats, oat flakes, packaged cereals or whole groats. All are rich in nutritional value and provide the basis of a healthy diet. They have a high carbohydrate content which supplies energy and a high protein content which is essential for growth. In addition oats are an excellent source of the B group of vitamins, especially thiamine, riboflavin, niacin and pyridoxine. The fats present in oats consist predominately of mono- and poly-unsaturated fatty acids which are less harmful than saturated fats.

Oats are a very good source of the soluble type of dietary fibre which is of particular benefit to sufferers from diabetes and heart disease. Medical trials have shown that this fibre can control and reduce harmful levels of sugar and cholesterol in the blood. Soluble fibre also helps other foods in the intestine release energy slowly and delays the onset of hunger; this factor, together with the low calorific value of oats, can be of benefit to slimmers.

In addition to the traditional porridge, present day oat cuisine features an extensive range of appetising dishes which includes pates, soups, quiches, stuffings, crumbles, cakes and desserts.

Recipes using Oatmeal

Grilled Trout or Herring in Oatmeal

One trout or herring per person
25-75 g (1-3ozs) medium oatmeal
lemon juice
salt and pepper

•

Wash filleted trout or herring and sprinkle with salt, pepper and lemon juice. Toss in oatmeal and grill (or fry if preferred) until lightly browned. Serve with small new potatoes, fresh garden peas and tomatoes sprinkled with chopped dill and parsley.

Skirlie

225 g (8 oz) medium oatmeal
125 g (4 oz) butter, dripping or olive oil
2 medium onions (finely chopped)
salt and pepper

•

Melt fat, add onion and brown lightly. Add oatmeal and stir over low heat until golden brown. Season to taste. Herbs, grated lemon or lemon juice may be added as variations. Traditionally served with mince and potatoes. Use as oatmeal stuffing for chicken or turkey.

Cranachan

275 ml (1/2 pint) whipping cream
1-2 tablespoons clear heather honey
1-2 tablespoons whisky
25-50 g (1-2 oz) lightly toasted fine oatmeal
1 tablespoon demerara sugar
125-150 g (4-6 oz) raspberries.

•

Whip cream, honey, sugar and whisky together. Fold raspberries into the mixture. Chill in refrigerator. Sprinkle oatmeal on top just before serving and decorate with raspberries. Yogurt may be substituted for half the cream.

Atholl Brose

275 ml (1/2 pint) double cream
125 g (4 oz) lightly toasted fine oatmeal
125 g (4 oz) clear heather honey
150 ml (1/4 pint) whisky

•

Beat cream to a light froth. Stir in honey and oatmeal. Just before serving add whisky and mix well. Place in frosted glasses and serve with shortbread. Small servings of this very rich dessert are sufficient.

Cheese Oatmeal Biscuits

225 g (8 oz) self-raising flour
225 g (8 oz) oatmeal
150 g (5 oz) butter or margarine
175 g (6 oz) grated cheese
1 teaspoon salt

•

Mix flour, oatmeal and salt. Rub in fat. Add cheese and enough water to make a stiff dough. Roll out and cut into rounds. Bake in moderate oven for 15-20 minutes.

Oatmeal Gingerbread

175 g (6 oz) flour
50 g (2 oz) oatmeal
50 g (2 oz) light brown sugar
50 g (2 oz) butter, 1egg
2 tablespoons treacle
1 teaspoon ground ginger
1 teaspoon bicarbonate of soda
small amount milk to mix

•

Melt butter and treacle and add to mixed dry ingredients. Add egg and enough milk to give a pouring consistency. Line a flat tin with greased paper and bake in moderate oven for 20-25 minutes.

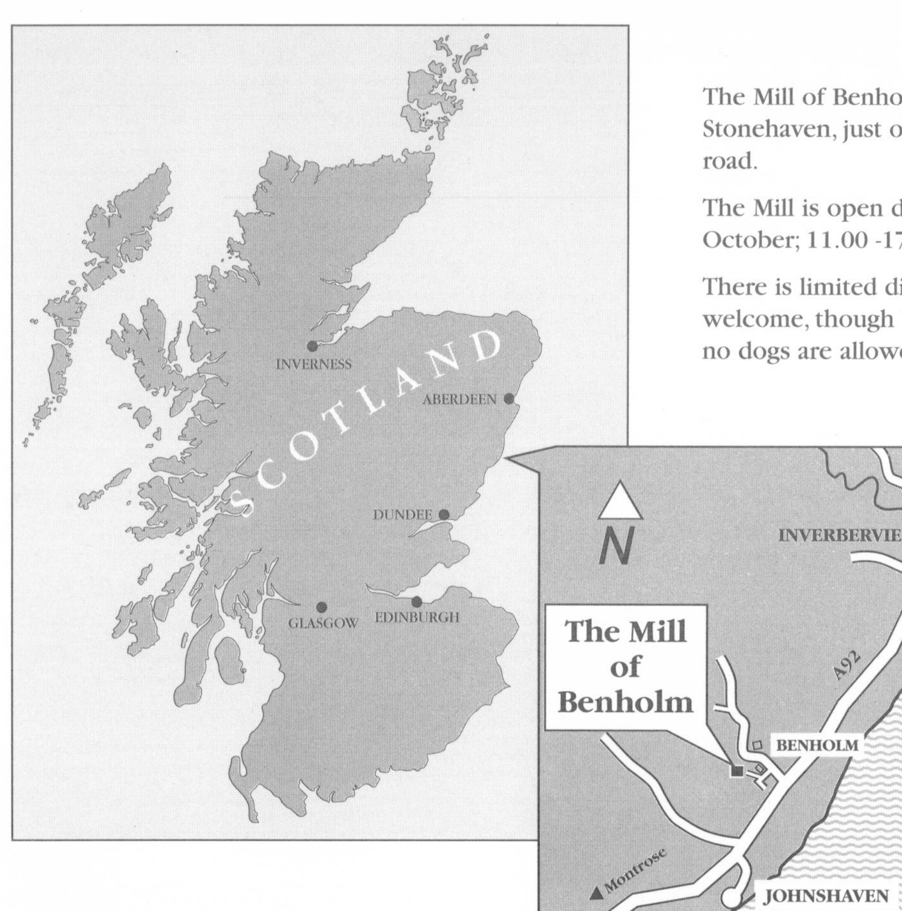

The Mill of Benholm is situated 13 miles south of Stonehaven, just off the A92 Aberdeen/Dundee coast road.

The Mill is open daily from Easter to the end of October; 11.00 -17.00 hours.

There is limited disabled access. Coach parties are welcome, though booking is advisable. We are sorry but no dogs are allowed at the mill.

For all further details please telephone:
01569 361969.

Mill of Benholm,
Benholm,
Montrose,
Angus,
DD10 0HT